MW00877780

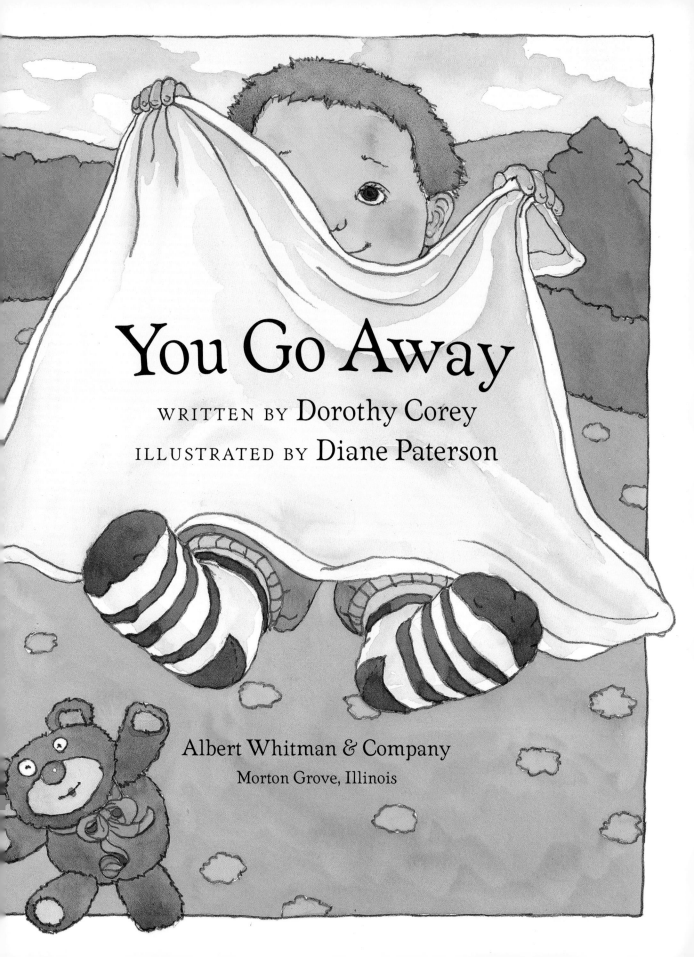

You Go Away

WRITTEN BY Dorothy Corey

ILLUSTRATED BY Diane Paterson

Albert Whitman & Company

Morton Grove, Illinois

To my grandchildren,
especially Peter and James,
to whom I haven't dedicated
a book so far. —D. C.

For Auntie, who came back and
stayed forever. —D. P.

Away!

Back!

Away!

Back.

You go away...

...and you come back.

I go away—

and I come back.

You go away?

You come back!

I go away,

and I come back.

You go away...

...and you come back.

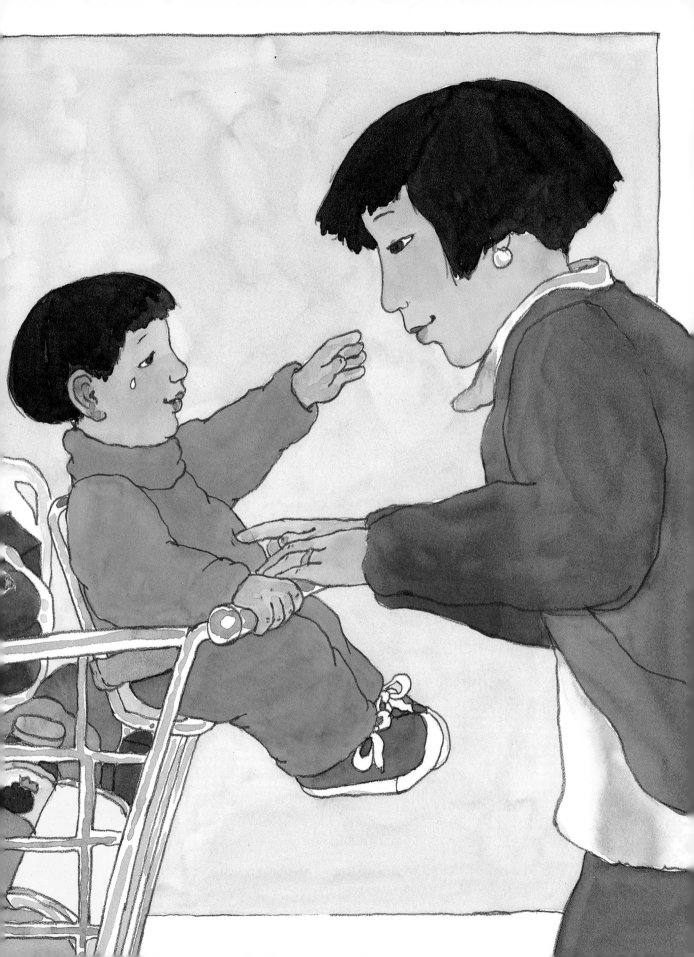

Away you go...

...and back you come.

You are going away.

You come back.

You are going far away—

you will come back!

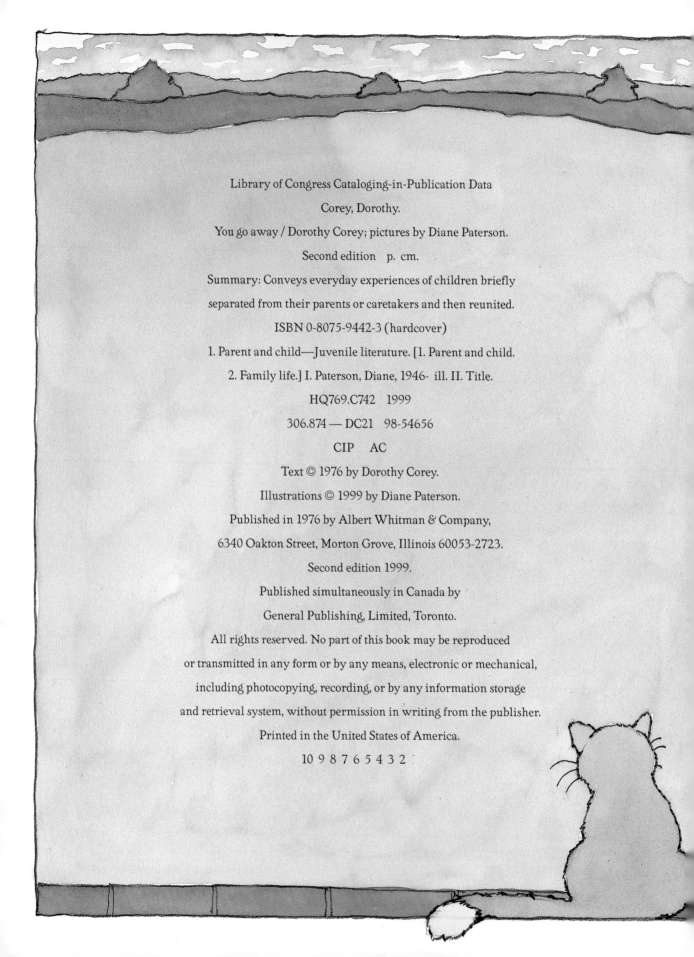

Library of Congress Cataloging-in-Publication Data

Corey, Dorothy.

You go away / Dorothy Corey; pictures by Diane Paterson.

Second edition   p. cm.

Summary: Conveys everyday experiences of children briefly

separated from their parents or caretakers and then reunited.

ISBN 0-8075-9442-3 (hardcover)

1. Parent and child—Juvenile literature. [1. Parent and child.

2. Family life.] I. Paterson, Diane, 1946- ill. II. Title.

HQ769.C742   1999

306.874 — DC21   98-54656

CIP   AC

Text © 1976 by Dorothy Corey.

Illustrations © 1999 by Diane Paterson.

Published in 1976 by Albert Whitman & Company,

6340 Oakton Street, Morton Grove, Illinois 60053-2723.

Second edition 1999.

Published simultaneously in Canada by

General Publishing, Limited, Toronto.

All rights reserved. No part of this book may be reproduced

or transmitted in any form or by any means, electronic or mechanical,

including photocopying, recording, or by any information storage

and retrieval system, without permission in writing from the publisher.

Printed in the United States of America.

10 9 8 7 6 5 4 3 2